# How to use this book

*Follow the advice, in italics, given for you on each page.*
*Support the children as they read the text that is shaded in cream.*
***Praise*** *the children at every step!*

*Detailed guidance is provided in the Read Write Inc. Phonics Handbook*

## 9 reading activities

*Children:*
*Practise reading the speed sounds.*
*Read the green, red and challenge words for the story.*
*Listen as you read the introduction.*
*Discuss the vocabulary check with you.*
*Read the story.*
*Re-read the story and discuss the 'questions to talk about'.*
*Read the story with fluency and expression.*
*Answer the questions to 'read and answer'.*
*Practise reading the speed words.*

D0326104

# Speed sounds

## Consonants   *Say the pure sounds (do not add 'uh').*

| f<br>ff<br>ph | l<br>ll<br>le | m<br>mm | n<br>nn<br>kn | r<br>rr<br>(wr) | s<br>ss<br>se<br>(c)<br>ce | v<br>ve | z<br>zz | sh | th | ng<br>nk |
|---|---|---|---|---|---|---|---|---|---|---|

| b<br>(bb) | c<br>k<br>ck | d<br>dd | g<br>gg | h | j<br>(g)<br>ge | p<br>(pp) | qu | t<br>tt | w<br>wh | x | y | ch<br>tch |
|---|---|---|---|---|---|---|---|---|---|---|---|---|

## Vowels   *Say the sounds in and out of order.*

| at | hen<br>head | in | on | up | day<br>make | see<br>tea<br>happy<br>he | high<br>smile<br>lie<br>find | blow<br>home<br>no |
|---|---|---|---|---|---|---|---|---|

| zoo<br>brute<br>blue | look | car | for<br>door<br>snore | fair<br>care | whirl<br>nurse<br>letter | shout | boy<br>spoil |
|---|---|---|---|---|---|---|---|

*Each box contains one sound but sometimes more than one grapheme. Focus graphemes are **circled**.*

## Green words

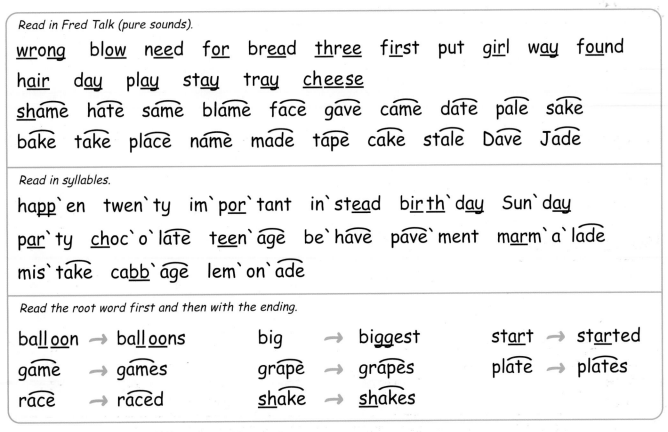

*Read in Fred Talk (pure sounds).*

wrong  blow  need  for  bread  three  first  put  girl  way  found
hair  day  play  stay  tray  cheese
shame  hate  same  blame  face  gave  came  date  pale  sake
bake  take  place  name  made  tape  cake  stale  Dave  Jade

*Read in syllables.*

happ`en  twen`ty  im`por`tant  in`stead  bir`th`day  Sun`day
par`ty  choc`o`late  teen`age  be`have  pave`ment  marm`a`lade
mis`take  cabb`age  lem`on`ade

*Read the root word first and then with the ending.*

ball oon → ball oons        big    → biggest         start → started
game     → games            grape  → grapes          plate → plates
race     → raced            shake  → shakes

**Red words**

why    brother
all    where    said    one

**Challenge word**

music

# Jade's party

### Introduction

*What's your favourite type of party?*
*What do you have to get ready if you are having a party?*
*Where do you go shopping for party things?*

*In this story, it's Jade's birthday and she's very excited.*
*She goes with her big brother, Dave, to the shops with*
*a shopping list. They have fun loading the trolley and*
*choosing napkins and balloons. But, when they get home*
*and unpack... something has gone horribly wrong...*

Story written by Gill Munton
Illustrated by Tim Archbold

# Vocabulary check

Discuss the meaning (as used in the story) after the children have read each word.

|  | definition: | sentence/phrase: |
|---|---|---|
| **group** | a pop group | |
| **raced** | walked really quickly | We raced along to the bus stop. |
| **stale** | food that isn't fresh | Out of the bag came a packet of stale fishcakes... |
| **past the sell-by date** | food that is stale | (past the sell-by date). |
| **sparklers** | a metal stick with special material that lights up and sparkles when lit | I had a chocolate cake with seven sparklers on it. |

*Punctuation to note in this story:*
*1. Capital letters to start sentences and full stops to end sentences*
*2. Capital letters for names*
*3. Exclamation marks to show anger, shock and surprise*
*4. 'Wait and see' dots...*

## Jade's party

My name is Jade.

It was my birthday on Sunday,

and I had a party.

But the party almost didn't happen!

I'll tell you why.

Dad made a shopping list.

twenty bread rolls

three packets of cheese

ten bags of crisps

ten milk shakes

ten cans of lemonade

a packet of napkins and a packet of plates

a packet of balloons

a tape of party music

a big chocolate cake

Dave's my teenage brother.
Dad asked him to take me to
the shops on the bus to get all
the stuff for the party.

We got a trolley, and Dave looked
at the list.

First, we went to the place where they bake bread.

Dave picked up twenty rolls and put them in the trolley.

(I picked up a currant bun, and hid it under the rolls.)

Then I found the cheese.

(Dave found the currant bun,

and told me to behave.)

Crisps …

milk shakes …

lemonade …

The trolley was filling up.

Party napkins, plates and a big packet of balloons.
Dave said he'd blow them up.

A tape – we got a good one by a new group.

And then the most important thing:
a chocolate cake (the biggest, with 'Happy Birthday' on top).

We went to the checkout to pay. A girl put all the
stuff in plastic bags and gave them to Dave.

Then we raced along the pavement to the bus stop.
We made up party games on the way.

Dad started to unpack the shopping.

Out came … a packet of stale fishcakes

(past the sell-by date) …

shampoo … a cabbage …

a can of hair spray … a bunch of grapes …

a jar of marmalade … and a jumbo pack of nappies!

Dad's face went pale.

"For goodness' sake, Dave!" he said. "What have you got to say?"

Dave said, "We must have picked up the wrong shopping by mistake.

Plastic bags all look the same to me. I'll take the blame, Dad.

I'll take it all back to the shops on Monday."

Well, it was a bit of a shame.

I hate grapes, and we didn't need hair spray – or nappies!

But it was okay in the end.

We had the party at a pizza place instead.

We had pizza, and chips, and pop.

Then, out came a man with a

birthday cake!

A chocolate one, with seven sparklers

on it. For me!

# Questions to talk about

*Re-read the page. Read the question to the children. Tell them whether it is a* **FIND IT** *question or* **PROVE IT** *question.*

**FIND IT**

✓ *Turn to the page*

✓ *Read the question*

✓ *Find the answer*

**PROVE IT**

✓ *Turn to the page*

✓ *Read the question*

✓ *Find your evidence*

✓ *Explain why*

**Page 9:**      FIND IT      *When was Jade's birthday?*

**Page 10:**     FIND IT      *What things on the shopping list can you eat?*

**Page 11:**     PROVE IT     *Where did Jade hide the currant bun? Why?*

**Page 12:**     FIND IT      *What do you think Dave said to Jade when he found the bun?*
                                            *What did he feel?*

**Page 13:**     PROVE IT     *How did Jade feel as the trolley was filling up?*
                                            *What sort of mood were they both in as they raced to the bus stop?*

**Page 14:**     PROVE IT     *Back at home Dad unpacked the shopping. Dad's face went pale.*
                                            *What was he feeling?*

**Page 15:**     PROVE IT     *How did they change their plans?*

# Questions to read and answer

*(Children complete without your help.)*

1. How many packets of cheese did Dad ask them to get?

2. Why did Jade put the currant bun under the rolls?

3. Why did Jade and Dave race along the pavement to the bus stop?

4. Why was Dad cross?

5. Why was it OK at the end?

# Speed words

| birthday | biggest | party | found | important |
| --- | --- | --- | --- | --- |
| hair | came | face | games | mistake |
| behave | lemonade | almost | why | anything |
| their | some | don't | all | going |